About this book

This is the story of young Matteo's meeting with an elderly Leonardo da Vinci and how he manages to overcome the rivalries between Renaissance artists and inspire the old master to paint again. Not all of the rivals are so easily won over, however …

Talking Points

1. Look at the cover illustration. How are the two younger characters looking at Leonardo?
2. What is perched on Leonardo's shoulder? How might the old master have come by such a creature? (see page 16)
3. In the blurb, what is meant by 'help Leonardo believe in himself again'?
4. The character list on page 2 shows us that some of the characters are real and some are fictional. As the tale progresses, think about why the author created Matteo and Niccolo for this story.

During Reading

1. Why does Niccolo hate Leonardo so much? (page 9)
2. On page 22, why are Primo and Secundo exaggerating about Leonardo's strange pet?
3. Why does Matteo think that Leonardo's studio is 'the most amazing studio'? (page 26)
4. Why is Michelangelo so angry on page 27? What makes him angrier?
5. What is it that inspires Leonardo to paint again? (pages 34–40)

After Reading

1. What did Matteo mean by, 'You're wrong if you think your paintings are no longer important …'? (page 30)
2. What is the point of Primo and Secundo in the story?
3. Thinking about everything that can be learnt about Leonardo in this book, ask the child what is the most amazing thing he did.

TreeTops GRAPHIC NOVELS

MASTER LEONARDO

OXFORD

MASTER LEONARDO

Written by

GLEN DOWNEY • JAYN ARNOLD

Illustrated by

MIKE ROOTH

This story is set during the Renaissance. Each chapter ends with a non-fiction page that gives more information about real people's lives and actual events at that time.

OXFORD

UNIVERSITY PRESS

LEONARDO DA VINCI

RAPHAEL

MICHELANGELO

MATTEO

NICCOLO

PRIMO AND SECUNDO

REAL PEOPLE IN HISTORY

LEONARDO DA VINCI (1452–1519): Leonardo was one of the most creative men who ever lived. He is famous for his paintings, sculptures, inventions and scientific writings.

RAPHAEL (1483–1520): A famous Italian painter and architect during the Renaissance.

MICHELANGELO (1475–1564): An extremely talented painter and sculptor.

FICTIONAL CHARACTERS

MATTEO: A 12-year-old boy who is Raphael's apprentice. He wants to know if the rumours he's heard about Leonardo are true!

NICCOLO: One of Raphael's workers who has a grudge against the old master Leonardo.

PRIMO AND SECUNDO: Thugs who work for Niccolo. They are never sure what he's up to!

Contents

Between the 14th and 17th centuries, Europe went through a period called the Renaissance, meaning 'rebirth'. This was a time of great advances in science, art and philosophy.

Rome was an important centre of the Renaissance. It was home to some of the greatest artists and thinkers in history. In 1513, three of Italy's greatest artists happened to be in Rome at the same time – Michelangelo, Raphael and Leonardo da Vinci.

TIMELINE

1452 »	1475 »	1483 »	1495 »	1501 »
Leonardo is born near Vinci, Italy. He will become known as Leonardo da Vinci.	Michelangelo is born in the village of Caprese in Tuscany.	Raphael is born in the town of Urbino, Italy.	Leonardo begins painting *The Last Supper*.	Michelangelo begins sculpting *David*, his most celebrated work.

By this time, Leonardo was already an old man. Younger artists such as Raphael were more popular than he was. Leonardo felt bitter and disappointed.

However, Leonardo's influence on other artists was much greater than he realised. In this story, Raphael's young apprentice sets out to reveal Leonardo's true legacy.

Leonardo da Vinci

This story is set in an actual time in history, although some of the events are fictional. Real events during this period are shown on the timeline below.

1503 ≫	**1504** ≫	**1513** ≫	**1514** ≫	**1519** ≫
Leonardo begins painting the famous *Mona Lisa*, completing it four years later.	Raphael travels to Florence to study the works of da Vinci and Michelangelo.	Leo X becomes pope when Julius II dies.	Raphael becomes one of the architects of St. Peter's Basilica. It will take 101 years to complete.	Leonardo dies in the town of Amboise, in France, at the age of 67.

1513: ROME, ITALY. A COLOURFUL PARADE TAKES PLACE BY COMMAND OF POPE LEO X!

MATTEO IS A YOUNG APPRENTICE OF THE GREAT ARTIST RAPHAEL.

ROME SEEMS LIKE THE CENTRE OF THE WORLD TO HIM!

MATTEO ENJOYS A TYPE OF STREET ACT CALLED *COMMEDIA DELL'ARTE.*

A BIG CROWD IS WATCHING THE PARADE.

WHO'S THAT MAN WITH THE HOOD?

THE MYSTERIOUS FIGURE LOOKS STRAIGHT AT MATTEO ...

GASP!

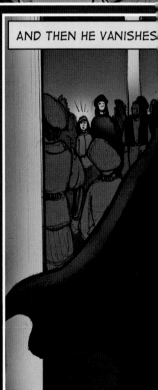

AND THEN HE VANISHES

DO YOU KNOW THAT OLD MAN, NICCOLO?

HMPH! IT'S JUST AN OLD NOBODY.

"THE WAY HE PREPARED HIS PAINTINGS WAS VERY SPECIAL."

I MUST MAKE SURE MY CALCULATIONS ARE JUST RIGHT.

"HIS FIGURES HAD GREAT DEPTH AND THEY LOOKED SO LIFE-LIKE!"

"HE SHOWED EMOTIONS BY USING SHADING TECHNIQUES."

THERE ... IT IS FINISHED!

SADLY, WE WON'T HAVE ANY MORE MASTERPIECES FROM LEONARDO.

WHAT? WHY NOT?

BECAUSE HE'S DECIDED NEVER TO PAINT AGAIN.

*I*n Italy, a type of street performance called *Commedia dell'arte* became popular during the 15th century. This form of theatre used witty dialogue, colourful costumes and physical comedy.

Troupes of actors performed on makeshift stages in towns and cities. They often worked without a script. *Commedia dell'arte* relied on stock characters that audiences could recognise easily.

Some of the most familiar characters were:

Arlecchino

Acrobat with a cat-like mask and multicoloured clothes; child-like but witty

Columbina

Maidservant who is quick thinking and solves everyone's problems

Pagliaccio

White-faced clown, dressed in loose white clothing; appears sad and dreamy

15

LEONARDO TELLS MATTEO ABOUT HIS LIFE.

I GREW UP IN THE GREAT CITY OF FLORENCE!

"WHEN I WAS 15, I WAS APPRENTICED TO THE WELL-KNOWN ARTIST VERROCCHIO."

BENE. THAT'S GOOD!

"WHEN I WAS 30 YEARS OLD, THE DUKE OF MILAN HIRED ME AS HIS ARTIST."

Raphael self-portrait

Raphael was a well-known architect and painter, and one of the most successful artists of the Renaissance. In 1508, he began work on the walls and ceilings of several rooms in the Vatican for Pope Julius II. These rooms are famous for their frescoes – they are an incredible achievement for a young man of 25.

Raphael learned from experienced and talented painters such as Leonardo and Michelangelo. He became a master at portraying the human form. His portraits captured the grace and personality of the people he was painting.

Raphael was a popular man who was always gentle and polite to those around him. Those lucky enough to work with him were deeply inspired by his teachings.

A ceiling fresco by ▶ Raphael, in the Vatican

MEANWHILE, NICCOLO AND HIS TWO FRIENDS ARE STILL RECOVERING FROM THEIR FRIGHT.

IT HAD FIRE COMING OUT OF ITS MOUTH!

AND DID YOU SEE HOW BIG IT WAS? AS BIG AS A BUILDING!

THAT OLD MAN HAS GONE TOO FAR THIS TIME.

IT'S CLEAR WHAT HE'S UP TO!

HUH?

HE'S GOING AGAINST NATURE ...

CONJURING UP MONSTERS!

WE MUST DEAL WITH HIM ...

ONCE AND FOR ALL!

LEONARDO AND MATTEO ARRIVE AT THE STUDIO.

I SELDOM HAVE VISITORS.

I, ER, I WANT YOU TO PROMISE ME SOMETHING.

OF COURSE! WHAT IS IT?

DON'T TELL ANYONE WHAT YOU SEE IN THERE. OK?

UH, OK!

I ... I CAN'T SEE ANYTHING!

BE CAREFUL AROUND HERE. THERE ARE THINGS I DON'T WANT KNOCKED OVER.

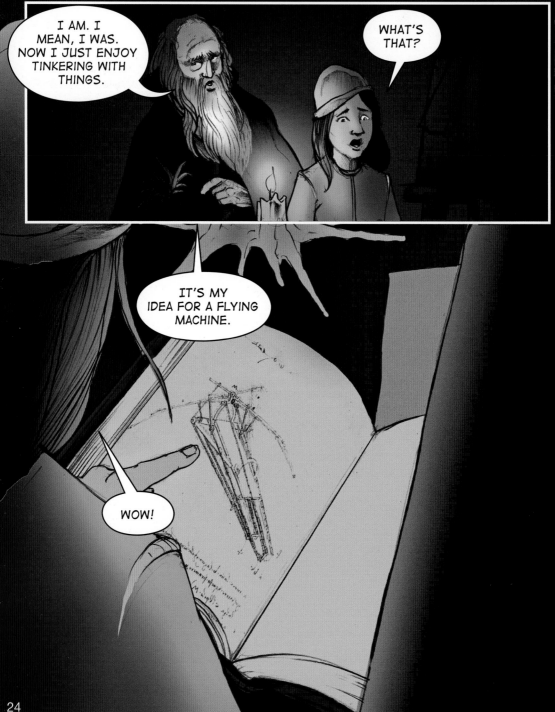

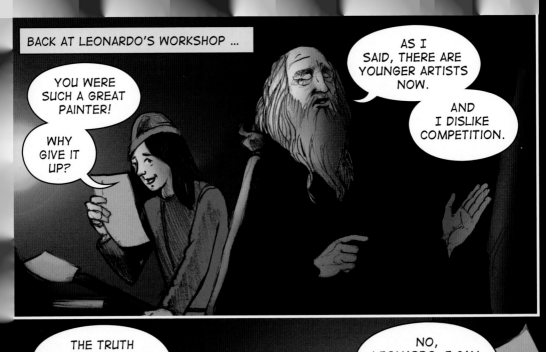

BACK AT LEONARDO'S WORKSHOP ...

YOU WERE SUCH A GREAT PAINTER!

WHY GIVE IT UP?

AS I SAID, THERE ARE YOUNGER ARTISTS NOW.

AND I DISLIKE COMPETITION.

THE TRUTH IS, MY BOY, I'VE LOST THE DESIRE TO PAINT.

THAT PART OF MY LIFE IS OVER. IT'S GONE.

NO, LEONARDO, I CAN PROVE TO YOU THAT YOU'RE WRONG!

I HAVE SEEN YOUR WORK IN MY MASTER'S ROOMS!

In the past, many cultures considered it awkward, clumsy or even unlucky to be left-handed. For these reasons, left-handed people were often forced to use their right hand to do things, even though it was more natural for them to use their left. Left-handed children, for example, were often made to write with their right hand, and were punished if they did not.

Left-handed people in society are at a disadvantage. Most things are designed for right-handed use, from machines and tools to household appliances such as scissors and can openers.

Despite attempts in the past to suppress the use of the left hand, there have been many famous left-handed people in history. The list includes not only Leonardo da Vinci, but also other great figures such as Einstein, Napoleon and Joan of Arc!

Recent studies have shown that left-handed people tend to be intelligent, artistic and musical. Many politicians, musicians and athletes are also left-handed.

MATTEO TRIES TO CONVINCE LEONARDO THAT HE'S WRONG.

YOU'RE WRONG IF YOU THINK YOUR PAINTINGS ARE NO LONGER IMPORTANT, MASTER LEONARDO.

COME ON, I'LL PROVE IT TO YOU!

WHERE ARE YOU TAKING ME, MATTEO?

YOU'LL SEE, MASTER LEONARDO, YOU'LL SEE.

DO WE HAVE TO GO QUITE SO FAST?

HMM, THIS IS AN EXCELLENT OPPORTUNITY.

THE OLD MAN HAS GONE OUT.

RENAISSANCE MAN

Leonardo da Vinci was a man of many talents. He is often called the 'Renaissance Man' because of his wide range of interests and his ability to think outside the box.

⚛ **SCIENCE**: He was interested in botany, astronomy and optics (the science of light).

⚛ **ART**: He was a prominent painter, draughtsman, architect and sculptor.

⚛ **ANATOMY**: He dissected many corpses in order to understand the human body.

⚛ **ENGINEERING**: He created designs for the helicopter, the calculator and the solar panel centuries ahead of his time.

MASTER RAPHAEL HAS SOMETHING TO SHOW LEONARDO.

COME THIS WAY, MASTER LEONARDO.

I BELIEVE YOU'VE MET THE ARTIST MICHELANGELO?

YES, I'VE MET HIM BEFORE. WE, ER, DON'T GET ON WELL..

YOU DON'T? WHY NOT?

THEY KNEW EACH OTHER IN FLORENCE. THEY WERE NOT EXACTLY GOOD FRIENDS.

COME AND SEE MICHELANGELO'S WORK IN THE SISTINE CHAPEL. I THINK YOU WILL LIKE IT.

OH, ALL RIGHT. BUT I HOPE WE DON'T RUN INTO HIM.

THERE ... FEAST YOUR EYES!

GASP!

OH! IT'S ... ALMOST TOO BEAUTIFUL TO LOOK AT!

SUDDENLY ...

MASTER LEONARDO! WE'VE BEEN LOOKING FOR YOU EVERYWHERE!

YOUR STUDIO — IT'S ON FIRE!

THEY RUSH TO THE OLD MASTER'S STUDIO!

OH, NO!

HOW DID THIS HAPPEN?

I SHOULD NEVER HAVE COME TO ROME!

ALL MY NOTES AND DRAWINGS ... UP IN FLAMES!

DON'T WORRY, LEONARDO ... I'LL GET THEM FOR YOU!

43

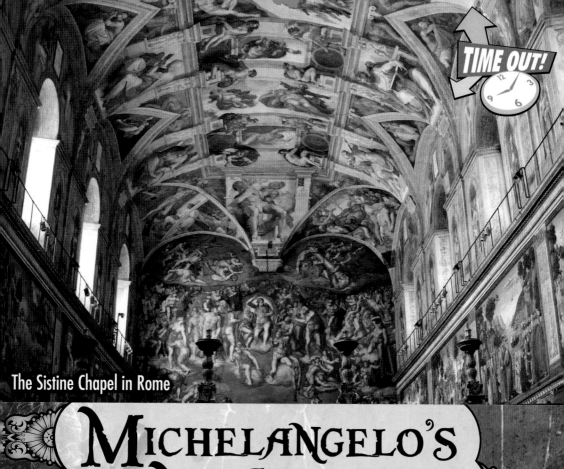

The Sistine Chapel in Rome

TIME OUT!

MICHELANGELO'S MASTERPIECE

*M*ichelangelo was a painter, sculptor, architect and poet. He was a rival of both Leonardo and Raphael. His figures have a quality called *terribilita*, meaning that they are powerful and breathtaking.

Michelangelo was asked to paint the ceiling of the Sistine Chapel in 1508. It was an extremely demanding job. For four and a half years, Michelangelo stood on a platform 18 metres high with his neck craned backwards while he applied paint to the wet plaster. It sounds like a good way to get a sore neck!

The finished painting is 39 metres long and features more than 300 figures. People agree it is one of the best works of art ever made!

Leonardo's Legacy

*As a well-spent day brings happy sleep,
so life well used brings happy death.*
Leonardo da Vinci

Mona Lisa

*L*eonardo da Vinci was one of the most gifted and creative people who ever lived.

By the time he died in 1519 at the age of 67, he had changed the world with his ideas and his art.

Leonardo was passionate about his many interests and worked extremely hard at all of them. Few people in history have moved so easily between science and art, and nature and invention. His genius was to see that everything was connected.

In art, Leonardo's achievements continue to dazzle the world. His paintings, especially the *Mona Lisa* and *The Last Supper*, still draw intense reactions from ordinary people. They also continue to fascinate the experts.

During his life, Leonardo influenced many of his fellow artists, including Raphael and Michelangelo. Today, his legacy continues to unfold. He was truly an inspired – and inspiring – person.

The Last Supper

INDEX

GLOSSARY

apprentice – a person who is learning a trade from an employer

architect – a person who designs buildings

curious – strange, unusual

imitation – a copy of something

inspire – to give a person creative ideas

quicksilver – mercury (a silvery metal that is usually liquid)

technique – the method of doing something